Music Together
Fiddle

Family Songbook

Illustrated by Jaime Kim

Hello, Everybody!

Welcome to a new semester of Music Together

This session, your family will add more than twenty new songs and dozens of expert-designed activities to your musical repertoire. For your child, the circle dances, fingerplays, and silly songs you'll share over the next few months are the beginning of a lifetime of musical connection. Dig into this book for inspiration to keep you humming and playing along all week.

Young children learn best from the powerful role models in their lives—that's you! By bringing music into your family's everyday life now, you will help your child become a confident music-maker just by having fun making music. There's no need to worry about your actual skills. What you'll be passing on to your child is the love of making music—while building lasting memories together.

Log on to musictogether.com/account to find music notation so you can play along, or to request additional Fiddle Song Collection CDs.

Hello Song

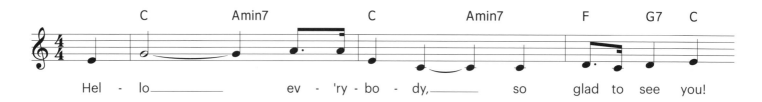

Hel - lo _____ ev - 'ry - bo - dy, _____ so glad to see you!

Hello everybody, so glad to see you!
Hello everybody, I'm so glad to see you!
Hello to _____, so glad to see you!
Hello to _____, so glad to see you, too!

Crawdad

You get a line, I'll get a pole, ho - ney.

You get a line, I'll get a pole, honey.
You get a line, I'll get a pole, babe.
You get a line, I'll get a pole, we'll go down to that crawdad hole,
Honey, oh baby mine.

Wiggle around up and down, honey...
In and out and 'round and 'round,
Honey, oh baby mine.

Get a guitar and play along, honey...
Then we're gonna sing our song,
Honey, oh baby mine.

Fiddle-i-o, fiddle-i-ay, honey...
Fiddle diddle diddle diddle diddle all day,
Honey, oh baby mine.

Let's go drivin' in the car, honey...
We can drive it really far,
Honey, oh baby mine.

Quietly we'll sneak around, honey...
We won't even make a sound,
Honey, oh baby mine.

Jumpin' up and down real fast, honey...
Wonder how long we can last,
Honey, oh baby mine.

We'll get a line, we'll get a pole, honey...
We'll go down to that crawdad hole,
Honey, oh baby mine.

The Sounds of Fall...

Lis - ten to the leaves drop - ping one by one! Ts, ts, ts, ts.

Listen to the leaves
Dropping one by one!
Ts, ts, ts, ts.

When we rake them up
We're gonna have some fun!
Whish, whish, whish, whish.

Listen to the birds
In the trees so high,
Chirp, chirp, chirp, chirp.

Don't you wish that you
Could flap your wings and fly?
Woo! Woo! Woo! Woo!

Apples and Cherries

Ap - - - - ples and cher - - - - ries,

and

Dee dee dee dee dee...

and

Vanilla   Strawberry   Chocolate

Yum Yum Yum Yum Yum...

Walking Song

(sing on "doo," "ba," or other syllables)

Doo Doo Doo Doo Doo...

A Ram Sam Sam

A ram sam sam, a ram sam sam, Gu-li gu-li gu-li gu-li gu-li ram sam sam!

A ram sam sam,
A ram sam sam,

Guli guli guli guli guli
Ram sam sam!

A rafi, a rafi,
Guli guli guli guli guli
Ram sam sam!

Fun Fact:
This song doesn't end on the home
note like other songs. Doesn't it
make you want to sing it again?

Old King Cole

Old King Cole was a merry old soul,
And a merry old soul was he.
He called for his pipe, and he called for his bowl,
And he called for his fiddlers three.

Old Queen Cole was a merry old soul,
And a merry old soul was she.
She called for her pipe, and she called for her bowl,
And she called for her singers three.

Princess Cole was a merry little soul,
And a merry little soul was she.
She called for her spoon, and she called for her bowl,
And she called for her trumpets three.

Young Prince Cole was a merry little soul,
And a merry little soul was he.
He called for his spoon, and he called for his bowl,
And he called for his drummers three.

Little Baby Cole was an itty bitty soul,
And an itty bitty soul was she.
She called for her spoon, and she called for her bowl,
And she called for her whole family!

Los Fandangos

Emin

B7

(sing on "lai" or any other syllable)

Did You Know?

A *Fandango* is a spirited courtship dance originating from Spain. Usually in triple meter, it is often accompanied by castanets or tambourine.

Goin' to Boston

Good - bye, Mom, I'm goin' to Bos - ton, Good - bye, Mom, I'm goin' to Bos - ton,

Goodbye, Mom, I'm goin' to Boston,
Goodbye, Mom, I'm goin' to Boston,
Goodbye, Mom, I'm goin' to Boston,
Earlye in the mornin'.
Let's all clap our hands now...

Doodle oodle oodle oo doo doo...

Goodbye, Dad, I'm goin' to Boston...
Let's all stomp our feet now...

Goodbye, friends...
Let's all dance around now...

Goodbye, Mom...
Goodbye, Dad...
Goodbye, friends...
Let's all wave our hands now...

Musical Parenting Hack:
This song can help with "goodbyes"
(or even "goodnights")...and it
works for grownups, too!

Can You Do This?

Can   you   do   this?   Yes I can, you bet I can!

Can you do this?   Yes I can, you bet I can!

Can you do this?   Yes indeed I can.

I can **clap** my hands,   You can **clap** your hands,

And **stomp** my feet!   And **stomp** your feet!

I can **jump** up high,   You can **jump** up high,

And **spin** around!   And **spin** around!

I can **touch** the ground,   You can **touch** the ground,

And **reach** the sky!   And **reach** the sky!

Can you do this?   Yes indeed I can!

Bela Boya

(sing on "na," "la" or any other syllable)

Fun Fact:
This is a Bulgarian folksong in $\frac{7}{8}$ meter. The Turkish word for asymmetric meter is *aksak*, which means "limping"—the way this song feels.

Sweet Potato

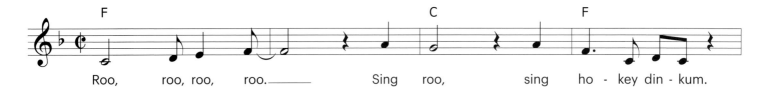

Roo,   roo, roo,   roo.————   Sing   roo,   sing   ho - key din - kum.

Roo, roo, roo, roo.
Sing roo, sing hokey dinkum.
Roo, roo, roo, roo.
Sing roo, sing roo.

Soon as we all cook sweet potatoes,
Sweet potatoes, sweet potatoes.
Soon as we all cook sweet potatoes,
Eat 'em right straight up.

Soon as supper's et Mama hollers,
Mama hollers, Mama hollers,
Soon as supper's et Mama hollers,
"Go straight to bed!"

Did You Know?

This simple tune about sweet potatoes has interesting roots (see what we did there?). It seems to be based on an old Creole proverb, *"Quand patate tchuite, faut mange li,"* meaning "when the sweet potato is cooked, it must be eaten," suggesting that one should act immediately when an opportunity arises.

The distinctive *habanera* rhythm heard throughout the song in phrases like "Soon as we all..." has African and Latin American origins and was a common accompaniment to dancing in late 18th-century New Orleans. Lively music-making was seen and heard in Congo Square near the French Quarter during the late 18th century. People of African heritage, both free and enslaved (who were allowed to express the music of their culture on Sundays under a French decree called *Code Noir*), gathered together to sing and dance.

These important cultural, musical expressions planted the seeds for and later influenced several American musical genres, including Jazz, Second Line, Ragtime, and even Classical. Composer Louis Moreau Gottschalk wrote his wildly popular *"fantaisie pour piano*, Op. 2" based on the simple Creole melody he'd heard as a child, *"Quan' patate la cuite,"* which we now know as "Sweet Potato."

Sweet Potato Pie

INGREDIENTS

- 1/3 cup (75 g) butter, softened
- 1/2 cup (100 g) sugar
- 2 large eggs, lightly beaten
- 3/4 cup (180 ml) evaporated milk
- 2 cups (240 ml) cooked, mashed sweet potatoes

- 1 teaspoon (5 ml) vanilla extract
- 1/2 teaspoon (2.5 ml) ground cinnamon
- 1/2 teaspoon (2.5 ml) ground nutmeg
- 1/4 teaspoon (1.25 ml) salt
- 1 unbaked 9 inch (23 cm) pastry shell

DIRECTIONS

Combine softened butter and sugar in a bowl. Add eggs and mix well. Add remaining ingredients and mix well. Pour into unbaked pastry shell. Bake at 425° (220° C) for 15 minutes. Reduce heat to 350°(175° C) and bake 35-40 minutes longer. Bake until a toothpick inserted in the center of pie comes out clean. Cool to room temperature and refrigerate. Serves 6-8.

Shady Grove

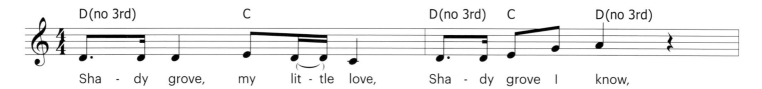

D(no 3rd)   C   D(no 3rd)   C   D(no 3rd)

Sha - dy grove, my lit - tle love, Sha - dy grove I know,

Shady grove, my little love,
Shady grove I know,
Shady grove, my little love,
I'm bound for the shady grove.

Singin' bird in the tree,
Singin' out so sweetly.
Singin' bird in the tree,
Sing your song to me.

Dream a little dream tonight,
Dream about tomorrow.
Dream a dream, oh so bright,
Dream away your sorrow.

Go to sleep, my little love,
Go to sleep, my darling.
Go to sleep, my little love,
I'll see you in the morning.

Did You Know?
Music holds our memories, and lullabies have a special kind of lasting power for children—especially when delivered by your loving voice.

Lauren's Waltz

"Get your instrument and play along!"

Here Is the Beehive

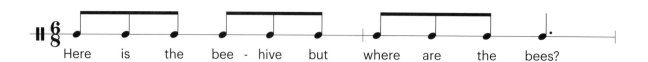

Here is the 🐝 but where are the 🐝🐝 ?

Hidden away where nobody

Watch and you'll 👁 👁 them come out of the hive 1, 2, 3, 4, 5!

Watch! And you'll see them come out once again, 6, 7, 8, 9, 10!

Marching and Drumming

Emin   G

Brrr - rum ba ba bum, ba bum, ba bum, ba ba___ ba ba,___

I've Got the Rhythm in My Head

Ding dong, I've got the rhythm in my head.

Ding dong, I've got the rhythm in my head.
Hot dog, I've got the rhythm in my head.
Ding dong, I've got the rhythm in my head.
Ding dong, ding dong, ding dong, hot dog!

Ding dong, I've got the rhythm in my hands...

Ding dong, I've got the rhythm in my toes...

Ding dong, I've got the rhythm in my feet...

Ding dong, I've got the rhythm in my head.
Hot dog, I've got the rhythm in my hands.
Ding dong, I've got the rhythm in my feet...

Ding dong, I've got the rhythm in my nose.
Hot dog, I've got the rhythm in my ears.
Ding dong, I've got the rhythm in my face....

Doo doo doo doo doodle doodle doo...

Hinei Ma Tov

Hi - nei ma tov u - ma nay - im, She - vet a-chim gam ya - chad.

Hinei ma tov uma nayim

Shevet achim gam yachad

Hinei ma tov,
hinei ma tov,
dai dai dai...

Did You Know?

The lyrics of this Hebrew-language song mean, "How good and pleasant it is for brothers and sisters to join together as one."

No More Pie

Oh, my!— Oh, my!— No more pie! No more pie!

Oh, my!
No more pie!

Pie's too sweet	Pie's too sweet
I want a piece of meat	I want a piece of meat
Meat's too red	Meat's too red
I want a piece of bread	I want a piece of bread
Bread's too brown	Bread's too brown
I think I'll go to town	I think I'll go to town
Town's too far	Town's too far
I think I'll take a car	I think I'll take a car
Car won't go	Car won't go
I fell and stubbed my toe	I fell and stubbed my toe
Oh, my!	Oh, my!
No more pie!	No more pie!
Boo hoo hoo!	Boo hoo hoo!
I miss you!	I miss you!
Boo hoo hoo!	Boo hoo hoo!
I miss you, too!	I miss you, too!
Tee hee hee!	Tee hee hee!
Stop ticklin' me	Stop ticklin' me
Oh, my!	Oh, my!
No more pie!	No more pie!

Butterfly

(sing on "doo" or "la")

Doo Doo Doo...

Dee Dee Dee...

Did You Know?

Children sing songs without words sooner (and more accurately) than they sing songs with lyrics. Playing with songs like this supports your child's first attempts at singing.

Mississippi Cats

Hey, who's that? A Mis-sis-sip-pi Cat! M-I-S-S-I-S-S-I-P-P-I!

Ba ba, ba ba ba da,
Ba ba, ba ba ba da.
Ba dooba daba dooba daba dooba ba,
Ba dooba daba dooba daba dooba ba.

Hey who's that?
A Mississippi Cat!
M-I-S-S-I-S-S-I-P-P-I!

A-ding-a dang-a ding-a dang-a ding dang dong,
Bing-a bang-a bing-a bang-a bing bang bong.
A-doob-a, a-doob-a a-doob-a da dee!
Scoo-ba-di bop-pa doo-ba doo-ba doo-ba doo-wee!

Singin' Every Day

Well I'm sing-in' e - very day and e - ver - y night.____

Ee-yo, ee-yo...

Well, I'm singin' every day and every night.
Well, I'm singin' every day and every night.
Singin' every day and every night.
Singin' every day and every night.

La la la...

La la la...

Hey, la la lay
Hey, la la lay

Well, I'm dancin' every day and every night.
Well, I'm dancin' every day and every night.
Dancin' every day and every night.
Dancin' every day and every night.

La la la...

Hey, la la lay
Hey, la la lay

Ee-yo, ee-yo...

This Little Light of Mine

This lit - tle light of mine,_____ I'm gon-na let it shine._____

This little light of mine, I'm gonna let it shine.
This little light of mine, I'm gonna let it shine.
This little light of mine, I'm gonna let it shine.
Let it shine, let it shine, let it shine.

This little face of mine...

This little nose of mine...

These little ears of mine...

These little hands of mine...

These dancin' feet of mine...

Shenandoah

Oh Shen-an-doah, I long to see you, Way a-way, you rollin' ri-ver.

Oh, Shenandoah, I long to see you.
Way away, you rollin' river.
Oh, Shenandoah, I long to see you.
Way hey, we're bound away.
Across the wide Missouri.

Did You Know?
This beautiful American ballad with Irish origins has been popular since the 1800s. Use our lullaby version to help ease the transition into dreamland.

Goodbye, So Long, Farewell

| D | D/C# | Bmin7 | D/A |

Good - bye, so long, fare - well, my friends,

Goodbye, so long, farewell, my friends,
Goodbye, so long, farewell.
We'll see you soon again, my friends,
So goodbye, so long, farewell.

Goodbye to _____, goodbye to _____,
Goodbye, so long, farewell.
Goodbye to everybody here,
Goodbye, so long, farewell.

Goodbye, so long farewell, my friends,
Goodbye, so long, farewell.
We'll see you soon again, and then
We'll make Music Together again.

And how 'bout a hug for your mom or dad,
Or the one who takes care of you?
And a hug or a handshake for your friends,
And then how 'bout one just for yourself, too?

Music Together Song Collections

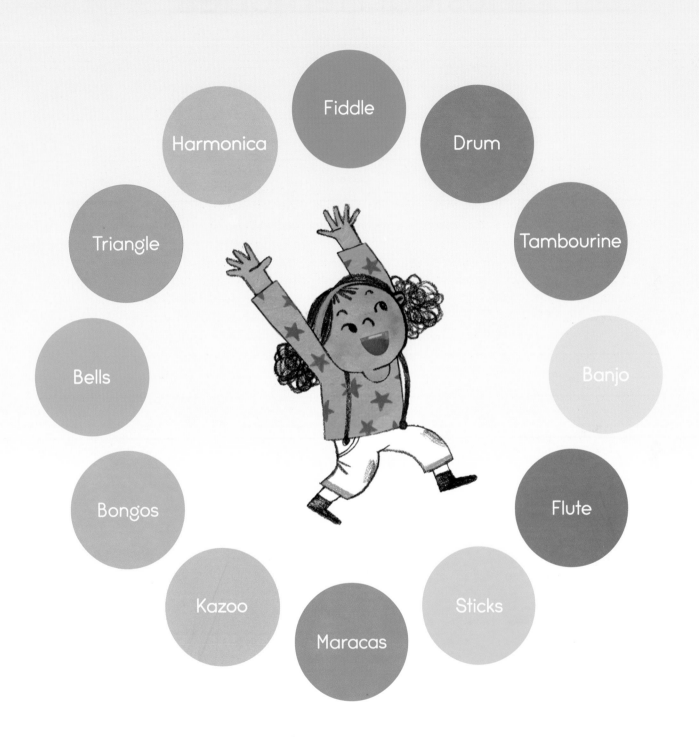

Fiddle

Harmonica

Drum

Triangle

Tambourine

Bells

Banjo

Bongos

Flute

Kazoo

Sticks

Maracas

Musical Memories

My child's favorite songs

_____

_____

_____

_____

Songs that saved the day

_____

_____

_____

_____

Our favorite made-up verses

_____

_____

_____

_____

Memorable moments from class

_____

_____

_____

_____

How we make music together at home

_____

_____

_____

_____

The Songs

Vocals: Lynn Lobban, John McVey, Gerry Dignan, Yvette Glover, Haley Carstensen, Megan Hayes, Anne Elise LeGall, Meggie McQuade, K. Guilmartin

Guitar: Joel Perry, John McVey

Acoustic bass: Matthew Parrish

Piano/keyboards: David Davis, K. Guilmartin

MIDI programming: D. Davis

Percussion: Ed Nardi, Glen Velez, K. Guilmartin

Fiddle: Tom Hanford

Violin, octave violin: Julie Lyonn Lieberman

Violin: Ruotao Mao

Cello: Mikyung Lee

Alto saxophone: Ken Ulansey

Trumpet: John Vanore

Harmonica: J. Perry

Recorder: Jill Crawford

Whistling: J. McVey

Produced and arranged by K. Guilmartin

Read about the singers on our recordings:
musictogether.com/singers

About Us

What Is Music Together®?

First offered in 1987, Music Together is based on the simple, yet revolutionary, idea that all children are musical and can learn to dance and sing as naturally as they learn to walk and talk. Our classes for children from birth through age eight—and the grownups who love them!—can be found around the globe. No matter where they live, Music Together families all sing and dance to the same music in the same fun, informal class setting.

Music Together Songs

The songs in each of our collections span a rich variety of tonalities, meters, and musical styles. And they're pitched in the perfect range for young voices. Fair warning: The music is just as catchy for grownups as it is for children. Parents have told us they've found themselves rocking out to their Music Together playlist—even when the kids aren't around!

To make it easy to take your Music Together songs wherever you go, be sure to download our *Hello Everybody* app and enter the code on the inside of this book. Don't leave home without it: Many a meltdown has been turned around with a favorite Music Together tune.

The Fun Continues

Your family's Music Together library will keep growing every semester. Over three years, you'll learn more than 200 songs. And when you cycle back to your first collection, you'll experience the familiar tunes in a whole new way.

- Read more about our philosophy:
  musictogether.com/about

- Download our *Hello Everybody* app:
  musictogether.com/app

- Music Together is worldwide! Find a class:
  musictogether.com/class-locator

- Buy kid-friendly instruments to play at home:
  musictogether.com/store

Committed to Research

We know that all children are musical because we've done our homework. As they developed the curriculum, Music Together coauthors Kenneth K. Guilmartin and Lili M. Levinowitz, Ph.D., realized they would have to look beyond accepted music education practices to the fields of early childhood development, neuroscience, and psychology. Music Together then led the way by applying developmentally appropriate practice to music-learning for very young children. The research continues today as we evolve, innovate, and stay on the cutting edge of early childhood music education.

Music-learning Is an Active Process

While developing Music Together, Ken and Lili discovered that children naturally teach themselves music through exposure and experimentation. Learning music, like language, requires participation. It's something you do, not something you just watch others do.

Children need to play *with* music before they can learn to *play* music. They take music in, through their ears, eyes, and bodies, and then play with it in their own way (think musical babbling). The more they play, the easier it is for them to move from babbling to speaking the language of music.

Because music-learning doesn't just happen in your Music Together class, we send the music home with you every semester. As you and your child play musically together, you naturally support their active, 24/7 learning process and their music (and overall!) development.

- More about the research behind Music Together: musictogether.com/about/research

- Learn about your child's musical development: musictogether.com/blog

- More about the benefits of music: musictogether.com/about/benefits

Music Together Program Authors
Kenneth K. Guilmartin
Lili M. Levinowitz, Ph.D.

Content Writers
Devi Bricker, Deanna deCampos

Contributing Writer
Jackie Freimor

Development Team
Devi Bricker, Lisa Chouteau, Marcel Chouteau, Susan Darrow, Deanna deCampos,
Lauren Guilmartin, Jenny Lantzer-Goings, Lili M. Levinowitz, Ph.D., Anne Sailer,
Julie Sansone, Mary Beth Weil

Design and Layout
CranCentral Graphics, Lambertville NJ, Dinardo Design, Concord MA,
Jennifer Leach Sanborn

Additional Art
Max Crandall

Production Assistance
Emily Heinz

Music Together Fiddle Family Songbook

Music Together Worldwide
225 Hopewell Pennington Road
Hopewell NJ 08525
musictogether.com